Star Light,
Star Bright

Hello and
Good-bye

Where
the Clouds
Go

HBJ
HARCOURT BRACE JOVANOVICH, PUBLISHERS
New York Chicago San Francisco Atlanta Dallas *and* London

Star Light, Star Bright

ODYSSEY **An HBJ Literature Program**

Sam Leaton Sebesta

Consultants

Elaine M. Aoki
Willard E. Bill
Sonya Blackman
Sylvia Engdahl
Carolyn Horovitz
Myra Cohn Livingston
Daphne P. Muse
Barre Toelken

Printed in the United States of America

ISBN 0–15–333350–2

Acknowledgments

For permission to reprint copyrighted material, grateful acknowledgment is made to the following sources:

Atheneum Publishers: "Wishing" from *There Is No Rhyme for Silver* by Eve Merriam. Copyright © 1962 by Eve Merriam.
Thomas Y. Crowell: "Knock, Knock" from *Father Fox's Pennyrhymes* by Clyde Watson. Text copyright © 1971 by Clyde Watson. "Riddle me, riddle me, what is that" from *The Golden Flute.*
William Heinemann Ltd. Publishers: "A,B,C, tumble down D" from *Cakes and Custard* edited by Brian Alderson.
Lothrop, Lee and Shepard Company: "Higher than a house," a Mother Goose rhyme, as reprinted from *The Arbuthnot Anthology of Children's Literature* by May Hill Arbuthnot.
Oxford University Press: "Rain on the green grass" from *The Oxford Dictionary of Nursery Rhymes* edited by Iona and Peter Opie (1951). "Sally go round the sun" and "Star light, star bright" from *The Oxford Nursery Rhyme Book* assembled by Iona and Peter Opie (1955).
Pantheon Books, a Division of Random House, Inc.: Condensed from *Goodbye, Hello* by Robert Welber. Copyright © 1974 by Robert Welber.
Random House, Inc.: "What kind of animals can jump higher than a house?" and "What goes up when the rain comes down?" from *Bennett Cerf's Book of Riddles* by Bennett Cerf. Copyright © 1960 by Bennett Cerf.
John Weatherhill, Inc.: "Why Rabbits Jump" from *The Prancing Pony* by Charlotte B. DeForest. Copyright 1967 by John Weatherhill, Inc.

Art Acknowledgments

Cover: Richard Brown.

Contents

Knock! Knock! Anybody There?

A rhyme by Clyde Watson

Knock! Knock! Anybody there?
I've feathers for your caps
And ribbons for your hair.
If you can't pay you can sing me a song,
But if you can't sing, I'll just run along.

Picture by Kinuko Craft

Happy Birthday to You

An old song

Happy birthday to you,

Happy birthday to you,

Pictures by Ted Rand

Happy birthday, Tina and Anna,

Happy birthday to you!

Rain on the Green Grass

An old rhyme

Rain on the green grass,
And rain on the tree,
And rain on the housetop,
But not on me.

What Goes Up?

A riddle

What goes up
when the rain comes down?

(An umbrella.)

Picture by Tony Kenyon

Sally Go Round the Sun

An old rhyme

Sally go round the sun,
Sally go round the moon,
Sally go round the chimney-pots
On a Saturday afternoon.

Picture by Jane Teiko Oka

Jack Be Nimble

A Mother Goose rhyme

Jack be nimble,
Jack be quick,
Jack jump over
The candlestick.

Picture by Jane Teiko Oka

Tell a Story
At Home

Picture by June Goldsborough

From Good-bye, Hello

A story in verse by Robert Welber

Pictures by June Goldsborough

A kitten goes creeping
Away from the rug.

Good-bye, Mother.
Hello, bug.

A mouse goes out
To climb and see.

Good-bye, Mother.
Hello, tree.

A bird begins
To try to fly.

Good-bye, Mother.
Hello, sky.

A squirrel comes running
Down the tree.

Good-bye, Mother.
Hello, bee.

A child is watching
Each little creature.

Good-bye, Mother.
Hello, teacher.

Questions

What did each one see?

1. I saw the tree bee bug

2. I saw the teacher tree sky

3. I saw the bug sky bee

4. I saw the bee teacher tree

5. I saw the bug sky teacher

Activity

Draw or paint a picture to show something *you* saw today.

Tell a Story
At School

Picture by Ted Carr

"Books We Read"
BILLY GOAT S GRUFF
THE THREE BEARS
THE THREE PIGS

A, B, C, Tumble Down D

A Mother Goose rhyme

A, B, C,
Tumble down D,

The cat's in the cupboard
And can't see me.

Picture by Sharon Harker

A B C Mystery

Nine letters are missing!

Raggedy Ann™ took the **A.**

Who took the other letters?

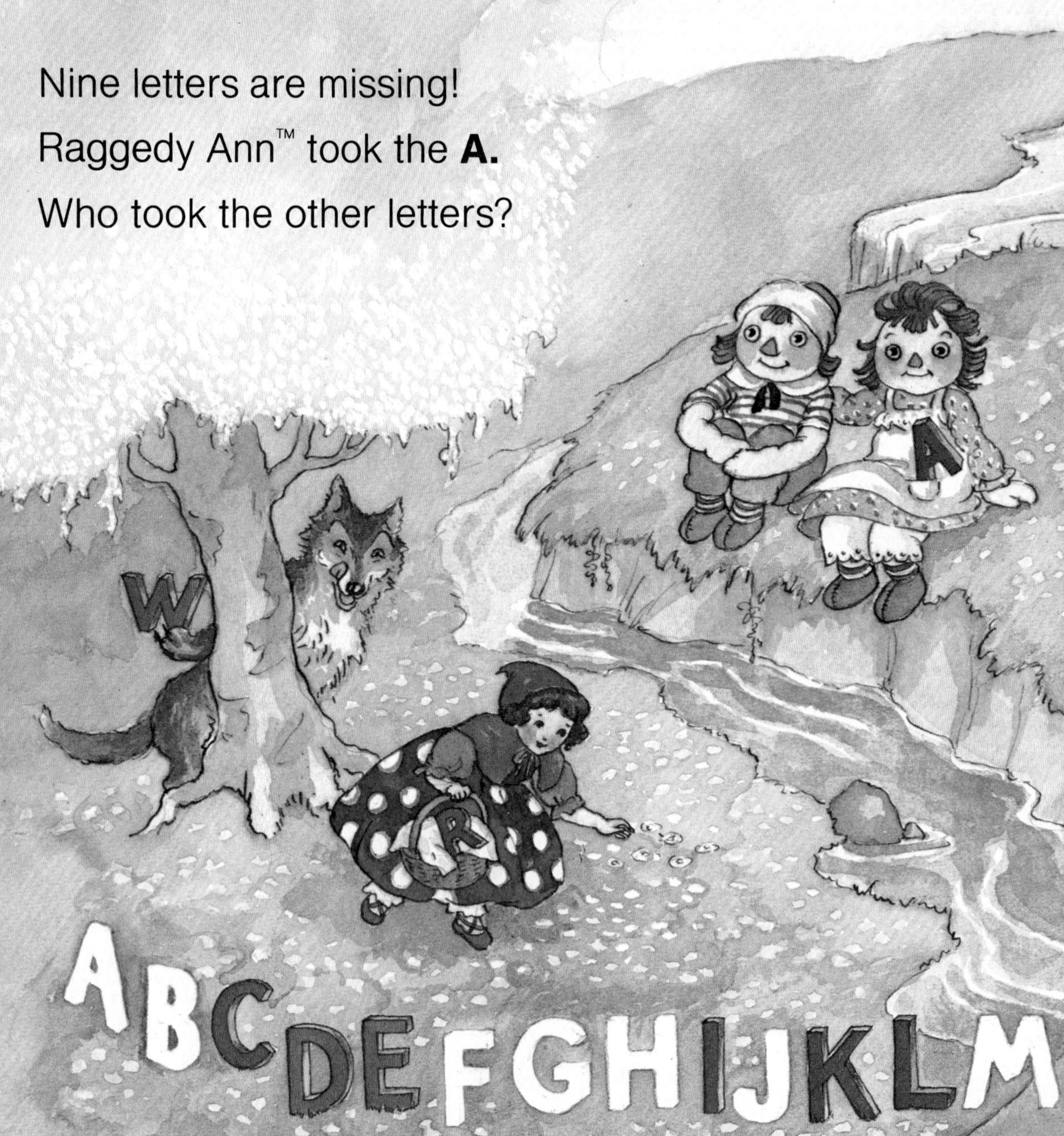

Picture by Kinuko Craft

Tell a Story
It's Halloween!

Picture by Kinuko Craft

Five Little Pumpkins

A rhyme

Pictures by Christa Kieffer

Five little pumpkins
Sitting on a gate,
The first one said,
"Oh, my, it's getting late."

The second one said,
“There are witches in the air.”
The third one said,
“But we don’t care.”

The fourth one said,
"Let's run and run and run."
The fifth one said,
"I'm ready for some fun."

"Oo-oo!" went the wind
And out went the light,
And the five little pumpkins
Rolled out of sight.

Riddle Me, Riddle Me

Two riddles

Riddle me, riddle me, what is that,
Over the head, and under the hat?

(Hair.)

What kinds of animals
can jump higher
than a house?

All kinds of animals.
Houses cannot jump.

Pictures by Stan Tusan

Why Rabbits Jump

An old Japanese rhyme

"Why are you rabbits jumping so?
  Now please tell why, tell why."
"We jump to see the big round moon
  Up in the sky, the sky."

Picture by Ed Taber

The Mitten

A Ukrainian folk tale retold in pictures by Willi Baum

Higher Than a House

An old riddle

Higher than a house,
Higher than a tree,
Oh, whatever can that be?

(Many answers,
such as a star,
the moon, a spaceship.)

Picture by Jane Teiko Oka

Star Light, Star Bright

An old rhyme

Star light, star bright,
First star I see tonight,
I wish I may, I wish I might,
Have the wish I wish tonight.

Wishing

A poem by Eve Merriam

If I could have
Any wish that could be

I'd wish that a dog
Could have me.

A B C D E F G H I J 1 2 3 4 5 6 7 8 9 0

Picture by Ted Rand